Thank you...

This Wet Play Today book is part of our growing range of educational titles. Most of our books are individual workbooks but, due to popular demand, we are now introducing a greater number of photocopiable titles especially for teachers. You may like to look out for:

WET PLAY TODAY for ages 5-7, 7-9, 9-11

READING FOR LITERACY for Reception
and for ages 5-7, 7-8, 8-9, 9-10, 10-11

WRITING FOR LITERACY for ages 5-7, 7-8, 8-9, 9-10, 10-11

SPELLING FOR LITERACY for ages 5-7, 7-8, 8-9, 9-10, 10-11

NUMERACY TODAY for ages 5-7, 7-9, 9-11

HOMEWORK TODAY for ages 7-8, 8-9, 9-10, 10-11

BEST HANDWRITING for ages 4-7, 7-11

To find details of our other publications, please visit our website: **www.acblack.com**

Contents

© Andrew Brodie Publications   www.acblack.com

WET PLAY TODAY

Contents

Shopping Wordsearch

Wendy went shopping and bought 21 items of clothing!
Can you find them hidden in this wordsearch?

C	O	A	D	D	R	E	S	A	R	F	B	O	R	S	H	T	S
A	N	R	S	R	A	Z	T	T	O	S	S	G	A	K	A	E	H
R	D	I	K	U	M	P	R	N	L	S	W	A	E	C	V	R	I
D	I	R	I	B	O	O	I	J	A	E	K	I	L	O	E	N	R
O	C	K	R	H	Z	T	H	U	M	M	B	A	L	S	X	O	P
R	E	S	T	R	O	U	S	E	R	S	F	G	D	I	Y	P	A
P	W	B	A	E	H	R	X	D	R	E	S	B	A	L	T	I	K
S	O	C	R	J	E	A	T	I	S	R	E	P	P	I	L	S	H
R	E	T	A	E	W	S	O	S	E	S	B	O	U	T	N	Z	C
P	V	S	E	R	G	A	C	K	N	L	X	I	N	A	R	D	M
J	U	M	P	A	D	S	T	E	Z	A	L	T	B	O	O	T	S
A	C	G	L	A	N	I	T	S	R	E	E	F	I	C	H	A	M
I	J	A	C	K	E	T	G	L	B	E	N	J	M	I	T	O	R
L	E	A	T	W	I	L	L	A	O	S	P	I	K	G	O	C	H
V	E	T	R	M	D	R	E	S	N	E	R	M	O	Z	J	N	A
E	G	A	W	S	K	I	R	X	C	O	R	D	U	B	K	I	N
S	L	H	A	N	D	B	A	G	P	H	L	H	V	J	E	A	F
T	S	U	M	C	I	H	L	E	G	S	Q	Y	S	S	E	R	D

SKIRT
SHIRT
BELT
TROUSERS
SOCKS
GLOVES
CARDIGAN

SWEATER
SLIPPERS
COAT
BOOTS
MITTENS
JEANS
JACKET

JUMPER
RAINCOAT
DRESS
HANDBAG
HAT
VEST
SHOES

© Andrew Brodie Publications   www.acblack.com   WET PLAY TODAY

Animal Wordsearch

Sam went to the zoo and found 20 animals.
Can you find them hidden in this wordsearch?

P	P	O	B	T	A	R	X	O	O	R	A	G	N	A	K
G	I	R	A	F	F	E	M	I	C	S	N	I	U	W	P
S	Y	A	T	I	N	T	R	E	L	L	E	D	F	O	Y
P	A	N	D	S	K	U	A	L	U	T	N	A	R	A	T
A	L	G	T	H	O	C	F	E	P	A	R	R	L	U	H
B	E	U	N	Z	L	E	O	P	A	R	D	R	A	G	O
N	A	T	U	B	Y	S	C	H	N	L	E	G	U	I	N
L	L	A	P	I	X	F	B	A	N	W	A	L	S	U	N
R	A	N	O	N	I	U	G	N	E	P	R	Z	N	C	F
I	K	L	Y	T	A	B	Y	T	I	G	P	E	A	R	O
N	C	A	M	E	L	Z	L	W	S	K	U	N	K	R	A
O	P	R	H	I	D	R	S	I	L	I	O	X	E	K	D
T	T	B	U	W	A	L	L	A	B	Y	P	G	R	A	N
M	Y	E	L	E	O	C	I	K	A	N	I	R	O	B	A
A	P	Z	B	I	R	T	O	H	D	T	O	R	R	A	P
R	A	F	F	B	Y	S	N	A	R	D	X	G	K	I	H

GIRAFFE
ORANGUTAN
FISH
KANGAROO
PYTHON
SEAL
TARANTULA

PENGUIN
LEOPARD
ELEPHANT
SNAKE
SKUNK
PANDA
CAMEL

ZEBRA
WALLABY
LION
TIGER
PARROT
BEAR

Five in a Row.

Decide who will be circles and who will be crosses.

Take it in turns to draw O or X on the grid. To win, you must have 5 circles or crosses in a row vertically, diagonally or horizontally.

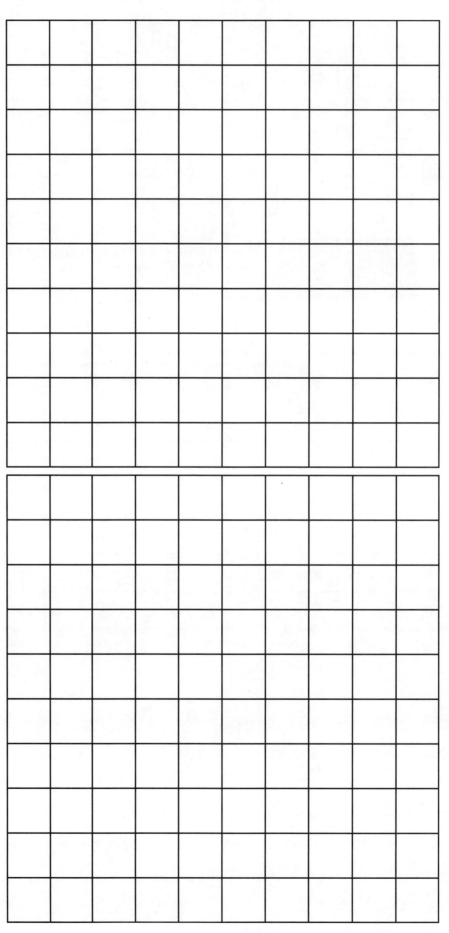

   WET PLAY TODAY

Number-jig (1)

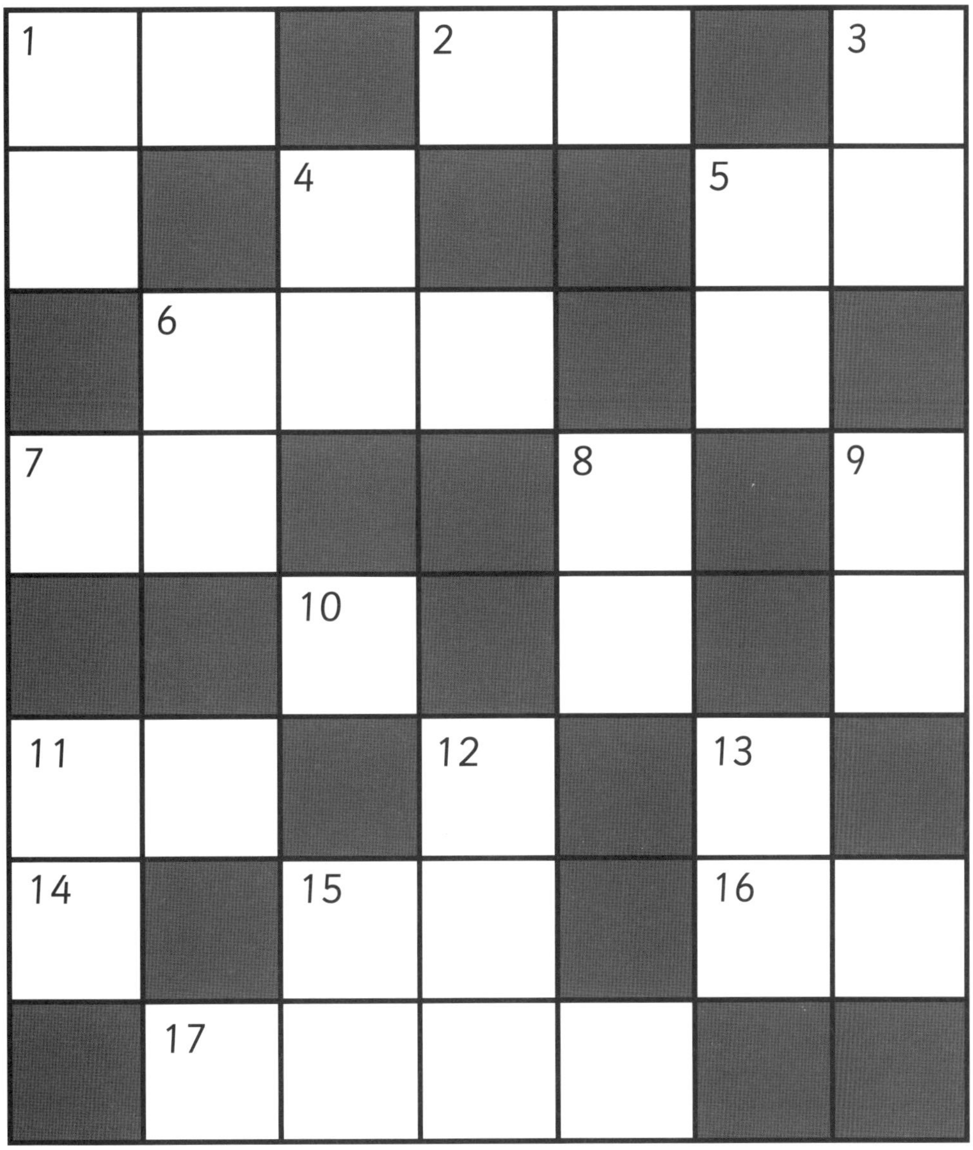

1			2			3
		4			5	
	6					
7				8		9
		10				
11			12		13	
14		15			16	
	17					

Across

1) 4 x 4
2) 28 – 4
5) 72 + 21
6) 900 – 44
7) 8 x 4
10) 400 – 397
11) 8 x 8
14) 98 – 4
15) 10 x 4
16) 7 x 10
17) 5000 – 4000

Down

1) 9 x 2
3) 11 x 3
4) 9 x 5
5) 9 x 11
6) 100 – 18
8) 8 x 2
9) 6 x 5
11) 32 x 2
12) 10 x 10
13) 9 x 3
15) 5 x 8

Can You Solve this Number-jig (2)?

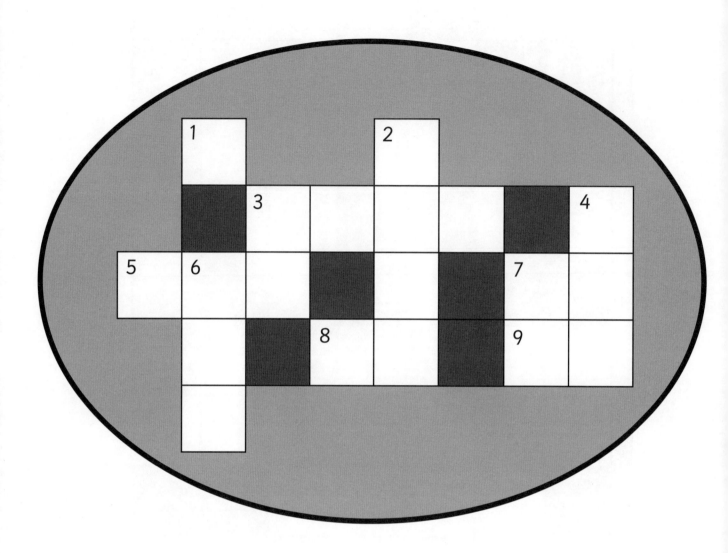

Across

1) 64 ÷ 8
3) 3248 minus 1120
5) subtract 247 from 638
7) 88 ÷ 4
8) 20 x 4
9) 9 x 9

Down

2) 5480 + 2810
3) 7 x 3
4) 11 x 11
6) 1848 ÷ 2
7) 140 ÷ 5

Mixed-up Countries

Rearrange the letters to make the names
of 13 countries.

R C A F E N   _ _ _ _ _ _

M R A E C I A   _ _ _ _ _ _ _

N D S E W E   _ _ _ _ _ _

Y E G R M N A   _ _ _ _ _ _ _

I N S A P   _ _ _ _ _

Y L T A I   _ _ _ _ _

L D S T I A W N Z R E   _ _ _ _ _ _ _ _ _ _ _

A A A T S I U R L   _ _ _ _ _ _ _ _ _

N I C A H   _ _ _ _ _

N A A P J   _ _ _ _ _

L R O T P G U A   _ _ _ _ _ _ _ _

I I D N A   _ _ _ _ _

E N W D Z A A N E L   _ _ _ _ _ _ _ _ _ _

Now try to make some mixed-up country
names for your friend to solve.

Code Machine

1. Cut out all 3 strips.

2. Join strips 1 and 2 together by gluing the shaded section and slipping it under section 2.

3. Place strip 3 above strips 1 and 2.

A	B	C	D	E	F	G	H	I	J	K	L
1	2	3	4	5	6	7	8	9	10	11	12	13	14

This example would be 'Code 3' because 'A' on the short strip is over the '3' on the long strip. To write the word 'ace' using 'Code 3' you would write 3, 5, 7. Make sure you put a comma between each number.

4. Check that your friends have a set of code machine strips and give them your coded message. Don't forget to tell them that you are using 'Code 3' or whatever your code. You can only choose a code between 2 and 26.

A	B	C	D	E	F	G	H	I	J	K	L	M	N
1	2	3	4	5	6	7	8	9	10	11	12	13	14	15	16	17	18

This example would be 'Code 5' because the 'A' is over the 5. To write the word ACE in 'Code 5' you would write 5, 7, 9.

Strip 1: 1 [shaded] 26 25 24 23 22 21 20 19 18 17 16 15 14 13 12 11 10 9 8 7 6 5 4 3 2 1

Strip 2: 2 52 51 50 49 48 47 46 45 44 43 42 41 40 39 38 37 36 35 34 33 32 31 30 29 28 27

Strip 3: 3 Z Y X W V U T S R Q P O N M L K J I H G F E D C B A

WET PLAY TODAY

Flying Superhero

Colour in this superhero with your favourite colours. Cut the shape out carefully and then cut along the dotted line x-y. Fold out the two wings - one to the front of the superhero and the other to the back of him or her. Put a paper-clip on the bottom between your hero's feet to make it spin better. Now throw it up in the air and watch it twist and twirl.

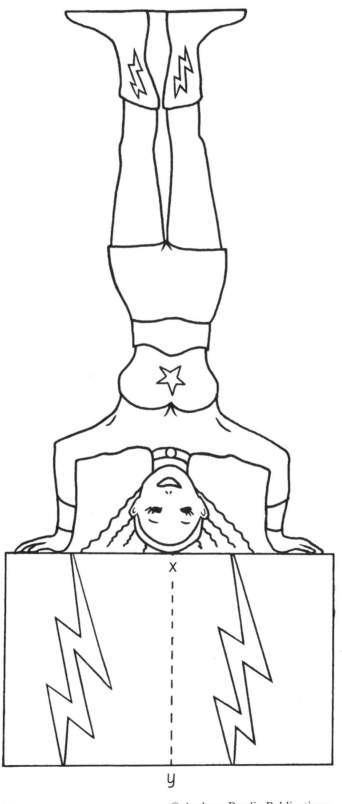

FUNNY FIGURES

1. Fold an A4 sheet of paper in half across the middle line.

2. Turn the paper sideways. Divide this into 4 equal strips and draw lines across, but stop before you get to the fold.

3. Cut through both pieces of paper along the lines as far as the dotted lines.
On the top section draw a head and neck.

4. On the second section draw the top part of a body.

5. On the third section draw the top half of the legs.

6. On the last section draw the bottom of the legs and the feet.

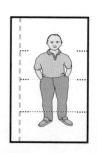

7. Now draw a different body in the same way on the strips that are behind. Put all the body parts in the same places but make them look different or funny. Move the strips to make your own funny characters.

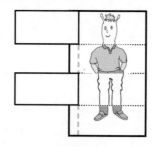

     WET PLAY TODAY

Draw the Pop Concert

Imagine you are at a pop concert of your favourite group.
Draw the scene you can see on the big screen.

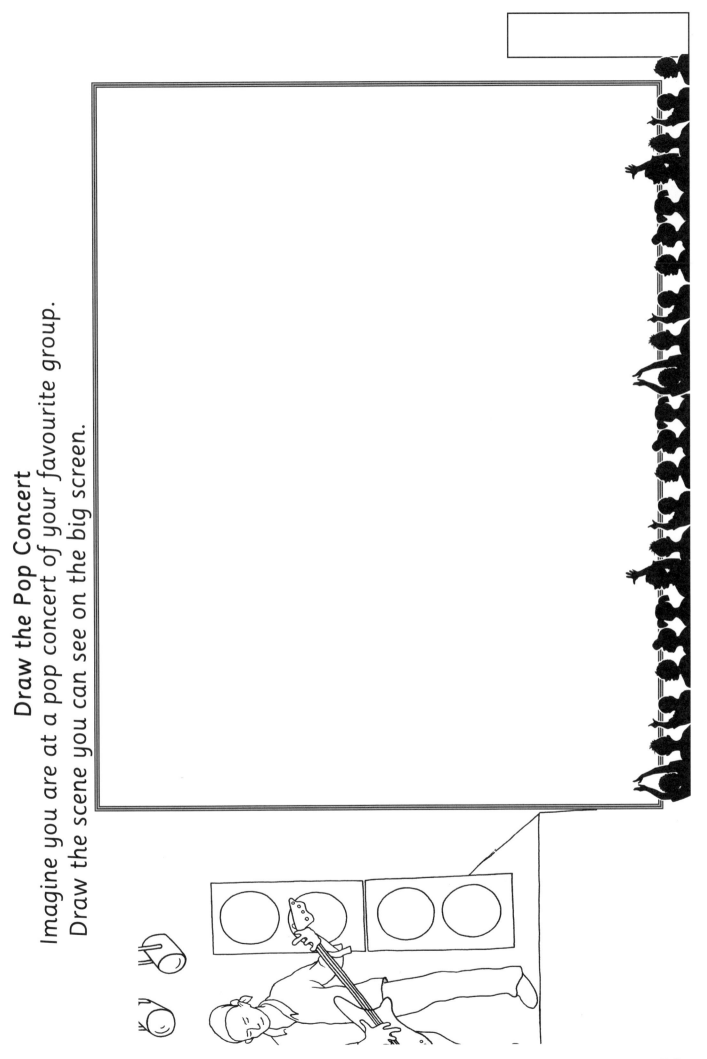

Football Wordsearch

R	O	T	A	T	N	E	M	M	O	C	A	K	T	T	A	K	C
P	P	E	N	A	F	L	T	S	P	O	C	M	I	U	Z	B	O
R	A	K	I	C	O	F	S	P	C	A	I	A	H	C	T	I	P
D	S	J	P	O	G	T	W	Y	T	M	D	S	J	L	U	O	E
O	S	P	W	V	O	C	S	T	A	D	I	U	M	I	N	A	N
A	A	O	C	O	A	M	A	W	U	L	S	O	O	B	N	T	A
J	R	A	B	B	L	S	D	U	T	S	C	D	R	W	E	N	L
O	T	A	M	V	K	B	T	C	I	U	K	S	I	B	L	U	T
W	R	O	R	B	E	S	C	O	R	P	U	N	D	I	T	A	Y
M	I	D	F	I	E	L	D	E	E	P	K	E	Y	L	A	O	G
P	H	E	O	M	P	O	R	N	E	O	I	E	N	G	M	I	M
C	S	T	A	C	E	O	E	R	B	R	L	R	M	E	Y	O	H
O	G	S	I	T	R	A	C	H	R	T	W	E	Y	E	L	I	R
I	S	N	G	A	N	H	N	E	R	E	R	F	W	H	O	T	D
N	I	A	H	T	U	O	E	Y	F	R	E	E	K	I	C	K	O
R	K	O	V	F	T	I	F	W	V	C	M	R	E	V	E	R	T
P	R	E	V	E	I	L	E	N	O	R	A	B	S	S	O	R	C
C	R	O	S	S	O	O	D	L	M	S	N	A	U	N	I	T	R

Can you find these football words in the wordsearch?

boots	commentator	penalty	midfield
pitch	pundit	free kick	attack
studs	referee	cross	supporter
stadium	goalkeeper	pass	save
tunnel	crossbar	defence	shirt

© Andrew Brodie Publications   www.acblack.com

WET PLAY TODAY

Moving Pictures

1. Cut out the 2 strips with the boy bouncing a ball.
2. Roll strip A tightly round a pencil.
3. Put strip A over strip B and hold them tightly at point X. Put your pencil into the curled up paper and slide it quickly from right to left so that the curl uncurls and curls back. You will see the boy bouncing the ball.
4. Now draw your own pictures on the remaining 2 strips and see if you can make them move.

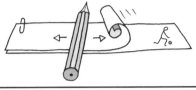

A	
X	

B	

A	

B	

Battleships

A game for 2 players.
Each player needs 2 grids.

1. Each player fills in their own navy's ships on one of their grids. This is done by writing letters in the squares.

Each player fills in:

   1 Battleship (B) which fills 4 squares.
   2 Destroyers (D) which fill 3 squares each.
   3 Cruisers (C) which fill 2 squares each.
   4 Submarines (S) which fill 1 square each.

The ships must be positioned in the grid so that there is 'water' (empty squares) all around them. Here is an example of a grid that has been filled in.

	1	2	3	4	5	6	7	8	9	10
A										
B		B	B	B	B		C			
C							C			
D		D		S					S	
E		D								
F		D		S			D	D	D	
G										
H			C		C	C				
I			C						S	
J										

Don't let your opponent see where you have positioned your ships.

2. Take turns trying to 'sink' your opponent's ships by giving a grid reference e.g. D2.

3. Your opponent must say 'splash' if this is an empty square, or Destroyer/Battleship/Cruiser/Submarine if the chosen square has any part of a ship in it.

4. Mark a D/B/C/S in the chosen square depending on which type of ship you have hit.

5. When you have found all the squares of a particular ship, your opponent must say Destroyer/Battleship/Cruiser/Submarine is 'sunk'.

6. The person who sinks all their opponent's ships first is the winner.

    WET PLAY TODAY

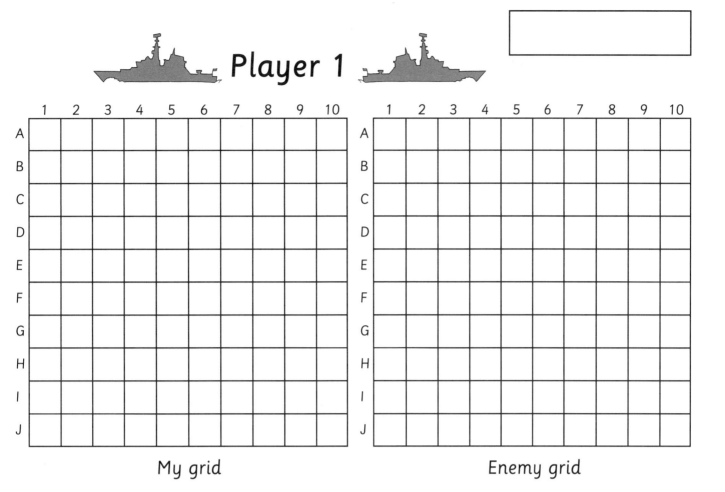

Player 1

My grid

Enemy grid

BATTLESHIPS GRID - CUT ALONG HERE

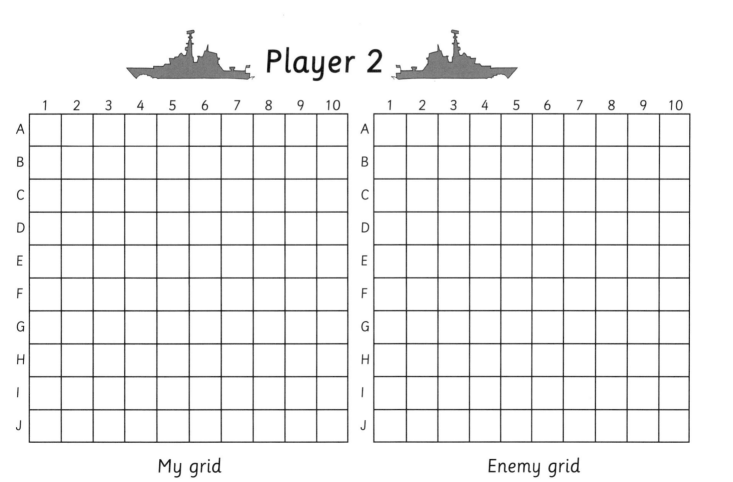

Player 2

My grid

Enemy grid

Crossword Sequences

	8	12	16	20		3	4		5		6

The grid is a number crossword with the following numbered cells: 1 (8, 12, 16, 20), 2, 3, 4, 5, 6, 7, 8, 9, 10, 11, 12, 13, 14, 15, 16, 17, 18, 19, 20, 21, 22, 23, 24, 25, 26, 27.

Across

1) + 4
3) − 177
7) x 2
9) − 9
11) − 5 then ÷ 3
12) x 3
14) x 1
15) − 14
17) ÷ 4
19) + 5 then ÷ 2
20) − 40
21) x 2 then + 5
23) + 11
24) − 9 then ÷ 2
27) − 8

Down

1) + 8
2) − 5
4) − 92
5) + 7
6) x 5
8) ÷ 5
10) ÷ 9
13) ÷ 3
15) + 26
16) + 6 then ÷ 3
18) + 8 then − 4
19) − 38
22) x 2 then − 1
24) − 118
25) − 2
26) + 15

The answers to this number crossword are all sequences of numbers.
The clue to 1 across is '+4' and the answer is 8 (+4), 12 (+4), 16 (+4), 20.
Now continue with 1 down. You need to work from the top left of the puzzle, only answering questions when you have the first number in the sequence.

    WET PLAY TODAY

ANSWERS

[1] 8	12	[2] 16	20		[3] 534	[4] 357	180	[5] 3		[6] 8
16		11				265		[7] 10	[8] 20	40
[9] 24	15	6		[10] 81		[11] 173	56	17	4	
32		[12] 1	[13] 3	9	27	81		24		
40			[14] 1	1		[15] 45	31	17		[16] 3
[17] 48	12	[18] 3		[19] 269	137	71	38			3
56		7		231		97				3
64		11		193		[20] 123	83	43		3
	[21] 5	15	35	75	155	315				3
	19			117		[22] 7				3
[23] 1	12	23		[24] 167	79	[25] 35	13	[26] 2		
	27		[27] 49	41	33	125	17	9	1	

Across

1) + 4
3) − 177
7) x 2
9) − 9
11) − 5 then ÷ 3
12) x 3
14) x 1
15) − 14
17) ÷ 4
19) + 5 then ÷ 2
20) − 40
21) x 2 then + 5
23) + 11
24) − 9 then ÷ 2
27) − 8

Down

1) + 8
2) − 5
4) − 92
5) + 7
6) x 5
8) ÷ 5
10) ÷ 9
13) ÷ 3
15) + 26
16) + 6 then ÷ 3
18) + 8 then − 4
19) − 38
22) x 2 then − 1
24) − 118
25) − 2
26) + 15

Boxes

A game for 2 players.

- ❏ Take it in turns to draw a line joining 2 dots. The dots must be next to each other either vertically or horizontally.
- ❏ The aim is to draw in a line that completes a box. Once you have done this you may put your initial inside it and that is now your box. You can continue your turn by drawing another line. If this also completes a box then you put in your initials and continue. If you do not complete a box, then it is your partner's turn, who continues in the same way.
- ❏ When all the dots are joined, count up the number of boxes each of you has their initials in, to see who is the winner.

© Andrew Brodie Publications   www.acblack.com   ⚘ WET PLAY TODAY ⚘

Picture Consequences (1)

A game for two players.

* Cut out the consequence strip from the second sheet. You will *need one* for each player.

* Fold the strip along the dotted lines.

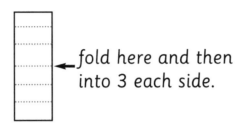

←fold here and then into 3 each side.

* Each person draws a head and a neck on the first section. It can be a human head, an animal head, an alien or anything that you can dream up. Make sure the lines of the neck just go over the fold. Fold back the first section so that it cannot be seen and swap it with your partner.

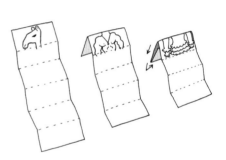

* On the second section draw the top half of the body and the top half of the arms (or wings or tentacles). Go a little way over the fold. Now fold this section back so it can't be seen and swap it with your partner.

* On the third section draw the bottom of the arms, the waist and the start of the legs. Swap with your partner again.

* On the fourth section draw the legs down to the knees then swap over again.

* On the fifth section draw the bottom part of the legs and swap again.

* On the last section draw the feet.

* Now open out your strip and see what strange characters you have drawn.

Picture Consequences (2)

This is an example of how your consequence strip could turn out.

Cut out this strip to do yours. ➜

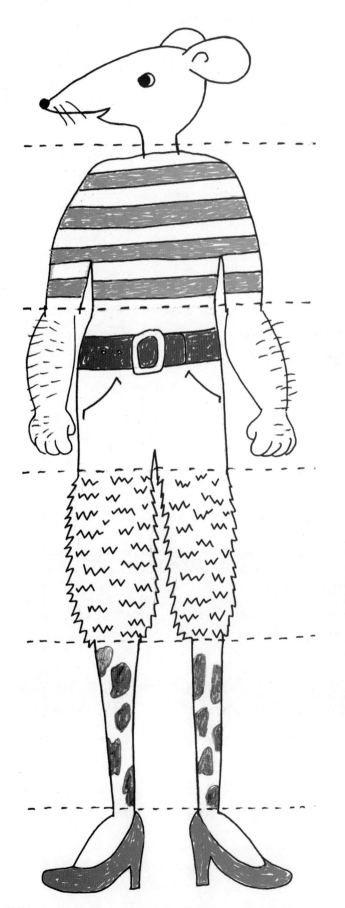

© Andrew Brodie Publications   www.acblack.com

WET PLAY TODAY

Amaze Your Friends With
Number Magic!

1. Cut out the four number sequences on this page.

2. Ask your friend to look at the squares and choose one number.

3. Ask him to name ALL the squares that his number appears on - A, B, C or D.

4. You will then be able to tell him his number.

5. Here's how it works. All you have to do is remember the top left hand number on each square i.e. A=1, B=2, C=4 and D=8. If your friend says his number is on A, B and D then you add up (A)1 + (B)2 + (D)8 = 11. So the number they have chosen is 11. It really works! Give it a try.

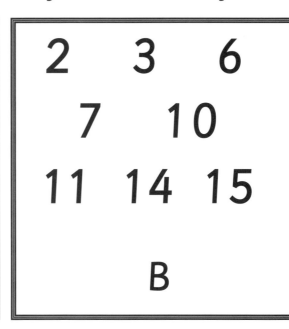

1	3	5
	7	9
11	13	15

A

2	3	6
	7	10
11	14	15

B

4	5	6
	7	12
13	14	15

C

8	9	10
	11	12
13	14	15

D

How to Make a Box (1)

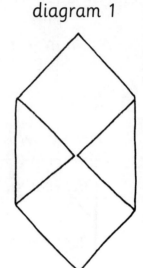

✳ Cut out the square on the other sheet of paper.

✳ Cut along the dotted lines only.

diagram 1

✳ Crease along line 1 at each corner and then
  open the paper out flat again.
  Fold back along line 2 on both sides.

✳ Turn over the paper so that it looks like
  diagram 1.

✳ Fold up along line 3 so that you are starting to
  form the box and it looks like diagram 2.

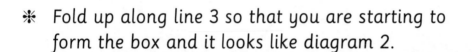

diagram 2

✳ Fold along all 4 lines marked 'line 4', tucking the
  flaps inside so that they cross over each other.
  See diagram 3.

✳ Fold up along line 5 at one end. Fold along line 6
  and bend the flap down over the overlapping
  sections to trap them. Now do the same the
  other end.

diagram 3

✳ Make sure the small triangular shapes sit
  flat on the bottom of the box and then stick
  them to the bottom to secure the box.

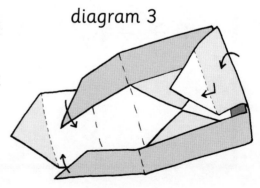

How to Make a Box (2)

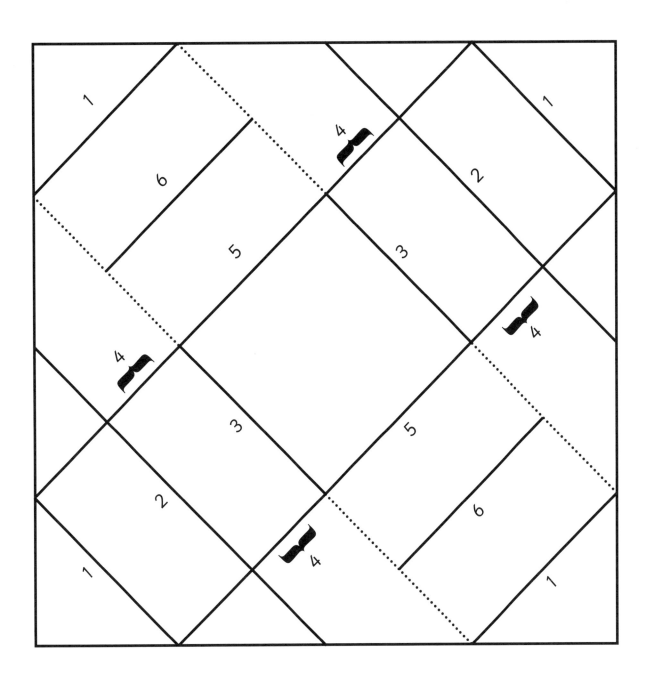

Knotty Problem

*Challenge a friend to hold the ends of a scarf and
then tie it in a knot without letting go of either end.*

This is how you do it.

* ☀ Place your scarf or large (clean) handkerchief - lengthways on a table.

* ☀ Sit on a chair with your scarf on the table in front of you.

* ☀ Fold your arms as in diagram 1.

* ☀ Without unfolding your arms, wiggle your hands until you have picked up
an end of the scarf with each hand.

* ☀ Keep firmly hold of the scarf ends and unfold your arms.
You will have tied the scarf in a knot.

WET PLAY TODAY

Follow the Map

Dear Kazim,

I'll meet you at the Sports Centre at 4p.m. Here is a map to help you to find it.

Follow the road from school and take the second turning left. Cross over the road at the crossing and go down Bear's Alley. Go over the bridge into the Park. Walk to the corner with the 2 trees and go out of the gate. Follow the path to the church. When you get to Hally Road turn left and go over the bridge. Turn left at the library. At the roundabout, take the second exit. The Sports Centre is the third building on the right.

See you there.

Love Abdul

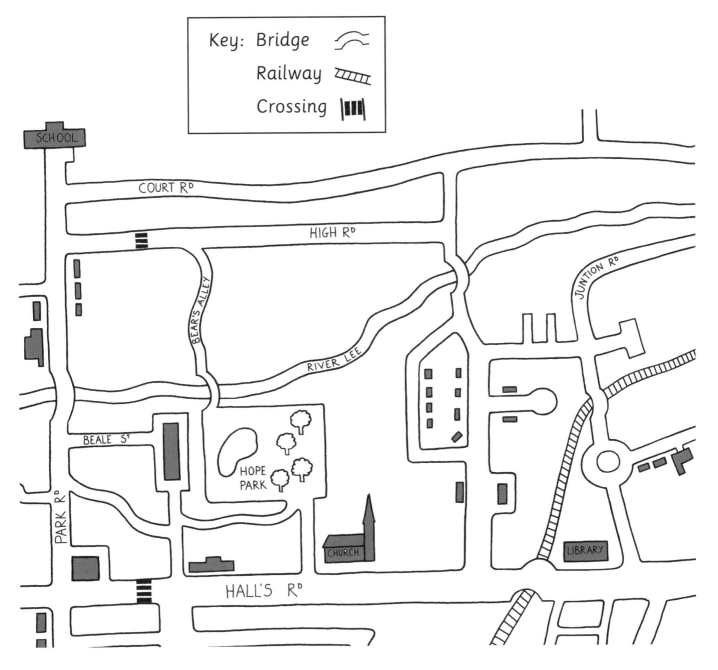

Key: Bridge
Railway
Crossing

SCHOOL

COURT Rᴰ

HIGH Rᴰ

BEAR'S ALLEY

RIVER LEE

JUNTION Rᴰ

BEALE Sᵀ

PARK Rᴰ

HOPE PARK

CHURCH

LIBRARY

HALL'S Rᴰ

Cat's Cradle (1)

You will need a piece of string about 1m 40cm long.
Make this into a loop with a small knot.

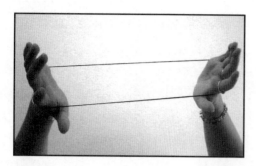

Loop the string around both hands. Make sure it goes between your thumbs. Stretch the loop out between your hands.

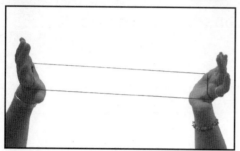

Loop the string round each hand so that there is a piece of string going across each palm.

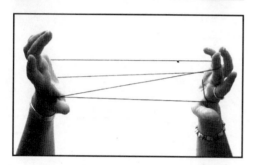

Slide your middle finger of one hand under the string across the palm on the other hand and pull.

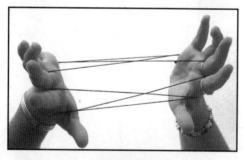

Do the same with the other hand. You have made a 'Cat's Cradle'. Your friend can now try to take the string from you to make a pattern called 'The Soldier's Bed'.

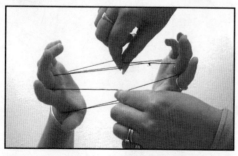

Player 2 pinches the X shapes from above. Make sure to pinch the X shapes the correct way. Look carefully at the diagram.

Keeping hold of the X shapes they pull the string and over their hands further out. This will make the string tight.

❀ WET PLAY TODAY ❀

Cat's Cradle (2)

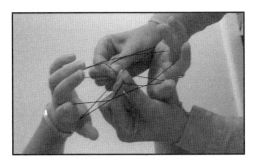

The next move is quite tricky. Keeping hold of the X shapes, they point their fingers downwards then scoop up the middle between the two horizontal strings. As they do this scooping movement, the first player lets the 'Cat's Cradle' slide off their hands.

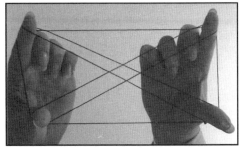

The second player now has the string on their hands in the shape of 'The Soldier's Bed'.

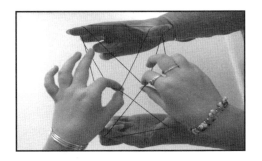

Player 1 now pinches the X shapes at the side. Make sure you pinch them as it shows in the diagram.

Keeping hold of the X shapes, pull your hands apart so that you pull the X shapes over the two horizontal strings.

Keeping hold of the X shapes, push your fingers under the two horizontal strings and up through the centre.

Open out your fingers. This shape is called 'Candles'. There are many more 'Cat's Cradle' patterns that you can find out about.

Sticks

A game for 2 players.

Take turns to cross out any number of sticks. The sticks must be next to one another in a row. The player who is left to cross out the last stick is the loser.

GAME 1

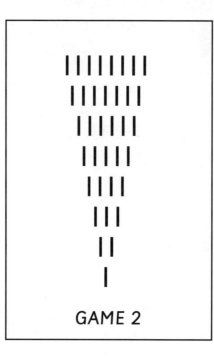

GAME 2

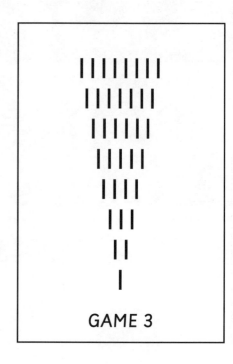

GAME 3

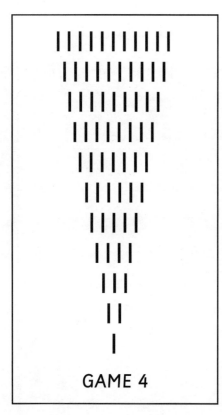

GAME 4

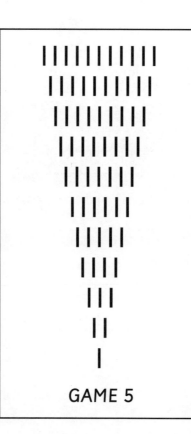

GAME 5

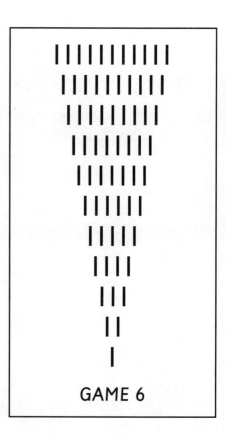

GAME 6

WET PLAY TODAY

Dots

- → Draw a small number of dots in a box (more than 3, less than 15).
- → Take turns to connect any 2 dots which do not already have 3 lines going to either one. Each dot is only allowed to have 3 lines attached to it.
- → When you have drawn your line, put a new dot in the centre of your line.
- → If a line goes through a dot, this is counted as having 2 lines going to it so can only have one further line joined to it.
- → The last one who can draw a line is the winner.
- → The first game has been started for you.

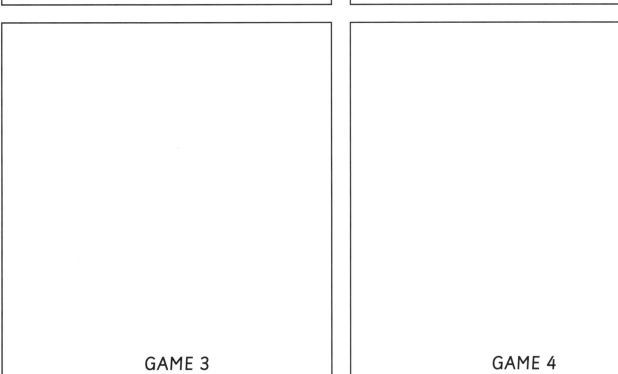

GAME 1

GAME 2

GAME 3

GAME 4

Connecting Paths
A game for two players.

The player who is 'Black dots' is trying to make a path from top to bottom.

The player who is 'White dots' is trying to make a path from left to right. ⟶

Decide who is going to be 'Black Dots' and who 'White Dots'.

Take it in turns to draw a line to join 2 dots of your own colour anywhere on the grid.

The dots must be next to each other either horizontally or vertically.

You can NOT cross your opponent's line.

To win you must make a continuous line either from top to bottom or left to right depending on your dot colour.

© Andrew Brodie Publications   www.acblack.com   ❀ WET PLAY TODAY ❀

Dice Cricket

A game for two players.
You will need 1 dice.

- Decide who will be Team A and who will be Team B.
- Make up names for your players and write them in the grid.
- Team A plays first.
- Throw the dice for player 1.
- Look at the scoring grid to see what player 1 scored and write it in the grid where it says '1st ball'.
- Throw again for his second ball unless he was out.
- If he is out on any ball, then Team A continues with their second player, and so on until all the team have had a turn. Each player has a maximum of 4 balls.
- Team B then take their turn in the same way.
- Each team adds up all their players' totals to see which team has won.

SCORING GRID

DICE THROW	RUNS
1	1 run
2	caught out
3	bowled out
4	4 runs
5	out - leg before wicket
6	6 runs

TEAM A

Name of Player	1st ball	2nd ball	3rd ball	4th ball	TOTAL
1					
2					
3					
4					
5					
6					
			TEAM TOTAL		

TEAM B

Name of Player	1st ball	2nd ball	3rd ball	4th ball	TOTAL
1					
2					
3					
4					
5					
6					
			TEAM TOTAL		

Dice Word

A game for two players.
You will need a pencil for each player and 1 dice.

🎲 Cut off the Record Sheet for Player 2 and give it to him/her.

🎲 Each player takes it in turns to find out their 6 letters.

🎲 Player 1 throws the dice and this tells him/her which box to look at. The second throw of the dice tells him/her which letter in that box is their letter. This is written on their Record Sheet.

🎲 Player 1 repeats this until he/she has six letters written down on the Record Sheet.

🎲 Player 2 does the same to get his/her six letters.

🎲 Each player then tries to make the longest word they can.

🎲 The winner is the player with the longest word.

(1)	A 1	A 2	B 3	C 4	D 5	E 6
(2)	E 1	F 2	G 3	H 4	I 5	I 6
(3)	J 1	K 2	L 3	M 4	N 5	O 6
(4)	O 1	P 2	Q 3	R 4	S 5	T 6
(5)	U 1	U 2	V 3	W 4	X 5	Y 6
(6)	Y 1	Z 2	S 3	M 4	T 5	L 6

Player 1 Record Sheet

My letters are: __ __ __ __ __ __

My longest word is: _____

Player 2 Record Sheet

My letters are: __ __ __ __ __ __

My longest word is: _____

    WET PLAY TODAY

Alphabet Atlas

Look in a World Atlas.

It's easy to find a place name that begins with the letter A.

Can you find a place name for every letter of the alphabet?

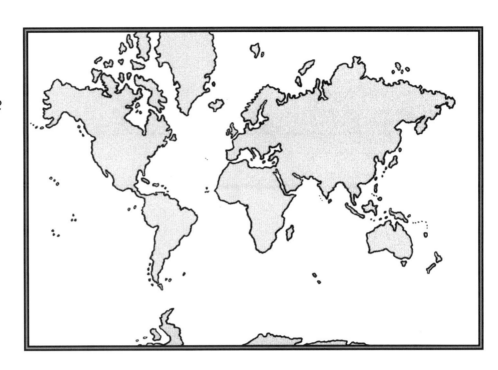

A ....

B ....

C ....

D ....

E ....

F ....

G ....

H ....

I ....

J ....

K ....

L ....

M ....

N ....

O ....

P ....

Q ....

R ....

S ....

T ....

U ....

V ....

W ....

X ....

Y ....

Z ....

Pangrams

Sentences that include every letter of the alphabet are called pangrams. Perhaps the best known pangram is this one:

> The quick brown fox jumps over the lazy dog.

How many times does each letter appear in this sentence?
Some letters appear more than once. You may like to cross the letters out as you count them. We have done the first four letters for you.

The quick brown fox jumps over the lazy dog.

a	b	c	d	e	f	g	h	i	j	k	l	m
1	1	1	1									

n	o	p	q	r	s	t	u	v	w	x	y	z

Now try to devise your own pangram
It's not easy.

WET PLAY TODAY

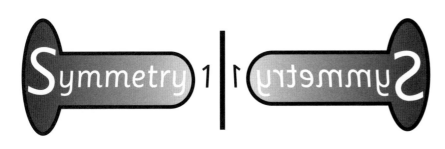
Colour the squares R red and B blue.

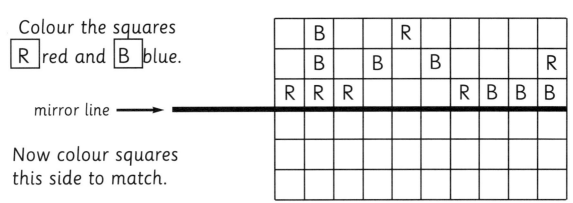

mirror line →

Now colour squares this side to match.

Colour the squares R red   B blue
                   G green   Y yellow

Now colour squares this side to match.

		B	B							
	Y	R	R	G						
R	G			B	Y					
R	G			B	Y					
	B			R						
		G	G							

Now use this grid to draw your own symmetrical pattern.

37

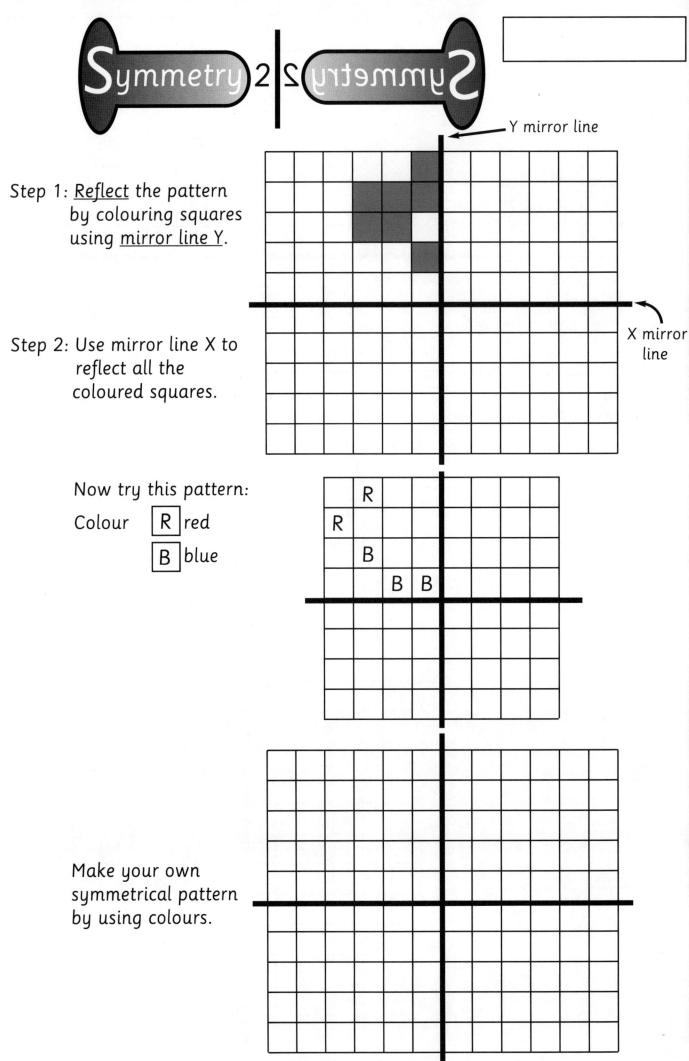

Symmetry 2

Y mirror line

Step 1: <u>Reflect</u> the pattern by colouring squares using <u>mirror line Y</u>.

X mirror line

Step 2: Use mirror line X to reflect all the coloured squares.

Now try this pattern:

Colour | R | red
        | B | blue

Make your own symmetrical pattern by using colours.

© Andrew Brodie Publications   www.acblack.com   WET PLAY TODAY

Word Square

☐ Make words of 3 letters or more.

☐ You must use letters in spaces joined by a side or by a corner. (So move horizontally, vertically or diagonally.)

☐ You cannot use a letter space more than once in any word.

☐ Use a dictionary to check that your words are correct.

☐ You should be able to find at least twelve words here. You could find as many as eighteen.

☐ The first one has been found for you.

I	N	T	E
P	U	P	L
T	L	I	L
N	E	G	I

PIN _____

_____

_____

_____

_____

_____

_____

_____

_____

_____

_____

_____

_____

_____

_____

Beginning in the top left-hand square, read around in a clockwise direction. Find two words to describe yourself!

Write them here.

I am an _ _ _ _ _ _ _ _ _ _ _   _ _ _ _

Word Wheel

○   Make words of 3 letters or more.

○   You must use letters in spaces which join each other (including diagonally).

○   You cannot use a letter space more than once in any word.

○   Use a dictionary to check that your words are correct.

○   You should be able to find at least twelve words here. You could find as many as twenty-four.

○   The first one has been found for you.

YOU _____

Read round the wheel to find a question. Write it on the line at the bottom.

Word Square and Word Wheel ANSWERS

I	N	T	E
P	U	P	L
T	L	I	L
N	E	G	I

PIN

PILL

PUN

GILL

GENT

PILE

PINT

LENT

NUT

PIG

LET

LIP

ILL

NIP

PUP

TELL

PUPIL

INTELLIGENT

I am an <u>i n t e l l i g e n t</u>   <u>p u p i l</u>

YOU

LIKE

WORD

GAMES

ORE

ROD

SAME

DEW

YOUR

SAG

SEEM

ROW

MEW

WED

DEED

SEED

DOES

DOE

DOOR

GAS

SEW

AIM

DEER

GAMES

ANSWER : Do you like word games?

Geography Crossword (1)

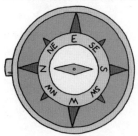

   WET PLAY TODAY

Geography Crossword (2)

Clues Across

1. North African river.
2. North African country.
5. The United States of _ _ _ _ _ _ _.
7. City found in Western Scotland.
8. Water between Europe and America.
11. Area of Northern Europe - includes Norway and Sweden.
12. Country to the west of Germany.
13. Continent where you will find Ghana, Morocco and Angola.
16. One of the Channel Islands.
19. A country and continent in the Southern Hemisphere.
23. Area around the South Pole. The _ _ _ _ _ _ _ _ _
24. City of Western India.
26. City of Western Australia.
27. Capital city of Italy.
28. Port of Eastern England.
29. Desert of Northern Africa.
30. Ocean, east of Africa.
33. Country, often called Holland.
35. Mount Etna is one of these.
36. You will find the river Rhine in this country.
38. Capital city of England.
39. Small island off the south coast of England.

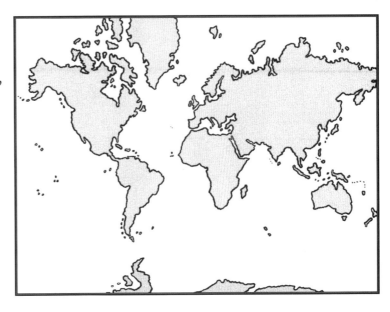

Clues Down

1. Country of Western Africa.
3. Irish river.
4. African country.
6. Port found in Eastern Scotland.
9. Eastern Mediterranean island.
10. This is full of maps.
11. Country to the north of England.
14. They speak French here.
15. Larger than a town.
17. Active volcano - found in Sicily.
18. City built as the Australian capital.
20. Capital city of Peru.
21. Middle Eastern country - has city of Baghdad.
22. Bird associated with New Zealand.
25. Continent including the Himalayas.
26. Country bordering Spain.
28. East coast Irish city.
30. European country - looks like a boot.
31. Opposite of south.
32. Capital city of France.
34. Opposite of north.
37. _ _ _ York, a city in the U.S.A.

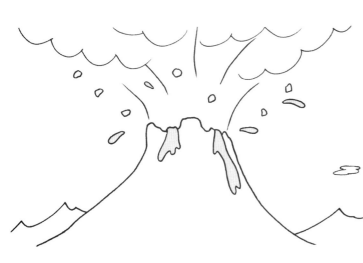

WET PLAY TODAY

43

Geography Crossword ANSWERS

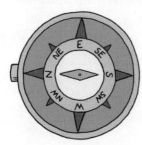

WET PLAY TODAY

Braille

In 1829 a Frenchman named Louis Braille invented a system of writing for blind people to read. It is known as the Braille alphabet. Each letter consists of a set of dots. These can be printed onto the paper by a press which raises the dots so that blind people can feel them with their fingers. The dot patterns are shown below but, on this paper, they are not raised up. Notice that some common words have their own dot pattern so that the writing is quicker to read.

The Braille Alphabet

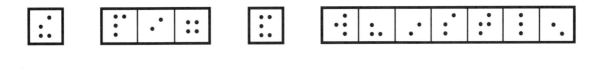

Here is a strange pub name.
We have written it out using the Braille dot patterns.
Try to work out the name.

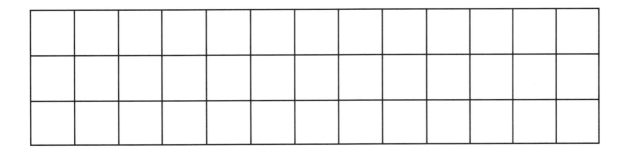

Write the name of your school using the Braille dot pattern.

General Knowledge Crossword

Try this general knowledge crossword. The clues can be found on the next page.

Reading from left to right, starting at the top, the letters in the grey squares spell out the names of six musical instruments.
Write them on the lines below.

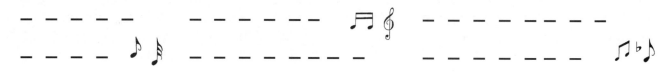

   WET PLAY TODAY

General Knowledge Crossword Clues

Clues Across

1. Sailed to America in 1492 (8)
3. Country - capital is Tunis (7)
4. A home for a dog. (6)
5. Keep fish in one of these. (8)
10. Find this on a fish. (3)
11. Person who enforces the rules of football. (7)
13. Take care - a wasp could do this to you. (5)
15. A table may have one at each corner. (3)
16. This will grow into an oak tree. (5)
17. A word meaning effort - also name of ship Captain Cook sailed to Australia. (9)
19. Heavy object used to stop a boat from drifting. (6)
21. The place you live is your _ _ _ _. (4)
23. Language in which the Qur'an is written. (6)
25. To lean. (4)
26. This ship sank in 1912. (7)
27. This happens when you are sleeping- an unpleasant one is called a nightmare. (5)
28. Monarch's headwear. (5)
31. Like cookies. (8)
33. Home for a bird. (4)
35. A form of 2 wheeled transport. (7)
36. A large group of musical instruments.
38. Heated bread. (5)
39. Very large sea. (5)
41. Large, deep-sounding brass instrument. (4)
43. First month of the year. (7)
44. Used to colour walls. (5)
46. Worn around the wrist. (8)
48. Water vapour. (5)
49. Precious metal. (4)
50. Casual footwear. (8)
53. Capital city of Scotland. (9)
56. A soft skinned, yellow orange, fruit. (5)
57. Not dirty. (5)
59. Twelve months. (4)
60. Low land, often with a river. (6)
61. See a play performed here. (7)
62. This flows through veins. (5)
63. King of the jungle. (4)
64. Country of South America. (9)
66. Planet in Solar System. (4)
67. Arm joint. (5)
68. Sugar will do this in hot drinks. (8)
71. Do this at a red traffic light. (4)
73. English monarch ruling from 1837-1901. (5,8)
76. Faith followed by readers of the Qur'an.
77. Clear (like window glass). (11)
79. Small bird, often seen in the garden. (7)
80. One quarter of thirty-two. (5)
81. A row of linked houses. (7)
82. A colour and a fruit. (6)

Clues Down

1. Letters that are not vowels. (10)
2. Part of a plant. (6)
3. Reddish brown colour or clay. (10)
4. Cutting tool. (5)
6. Line of people waiting. (5)
7. Like string but much thicker. (4)
8. Very small item. (9)
9. Look through these and things appear larger. (10)
12. Large grey pachyderm. (8)
14. Holy writing of the Islamic faith. (5)
18. Larger than a hamlet, but smaller than a town. (7)
20. A name given to a tropical forest. (6)
22. A type of small citrus fruit, similar to a tangerine. (8)
24. Famous queen in ancient Egypt. (9)
26. One more than nine. (3)
27. Use this to check spellings and meanings. (It could also help you solve this crossword!) (10)
29. A day of the week. (9)
30. This prevents sparks from the fire damaging the carpet. (9)
32. A historical object. (8)
34. The brother of one of your parents. (5)
37. Ten squared. (7)
38. This river passes through London. (6)
40. Large dangerous reptile. (9)
42. Designer of buildings. (9)
45. Worn around the neck. (8)
47. Worn to improve vision. (10)
51. Month preceding August. (4)
52. Country of North America. (6)
54. Ninety degrees. (5,5)
55. Smaller than a village. (6)
56. Rest your head on this. (6)
58. Capital city of England. (6)
65. Largest airport in the United Kingdom. (8)
69. Bright red. (7)
70. Imaginary line separating Northern and Southern hemispheres. (7)
72. Shape with 5 sides. (8)
74. Brass instrument found in the orchestra. (7)
75. Six sided shape. (7)
78. Ice will do this when warmed. (4)

General Knowledge Crossword ANSWERS

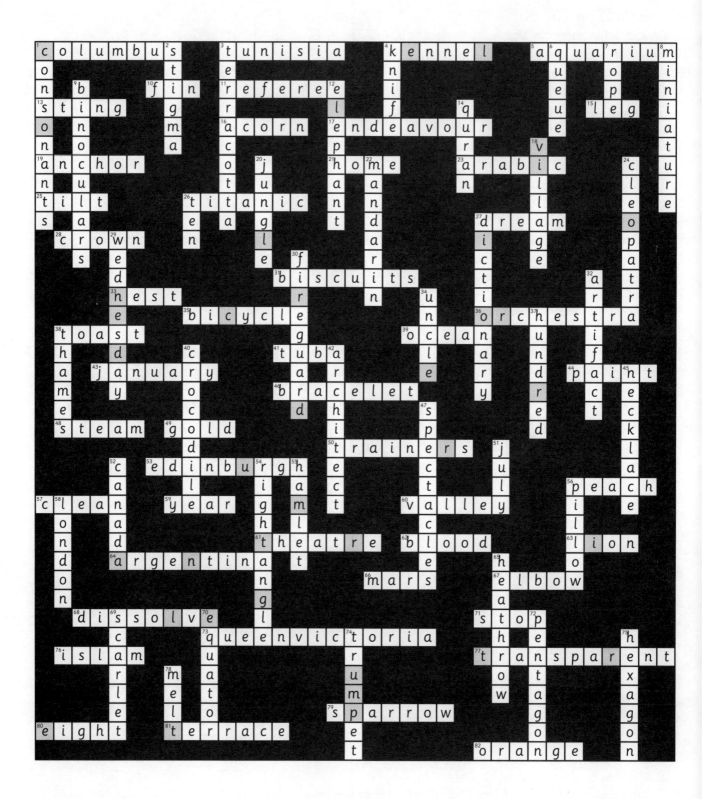

Instruments that should have been found:

cello   violin   recorder   drum   triangle   trumpet

         WET PLAY TODAY

Find the Animal

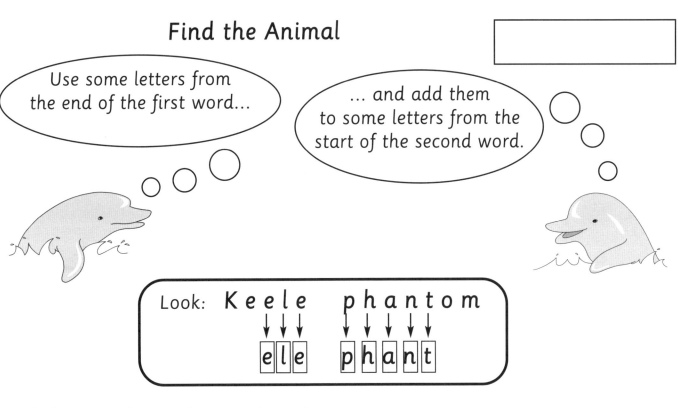

Use some letters from the end of the first word...

... and add them to some letters from the start of the second word.

Look: **K e e l e   p h a n t o m**

↓ ↓ ↓   ↓ ↓ ↓ ↓ ↓

e l e   p h a n t

Find the animal in each pair of words:

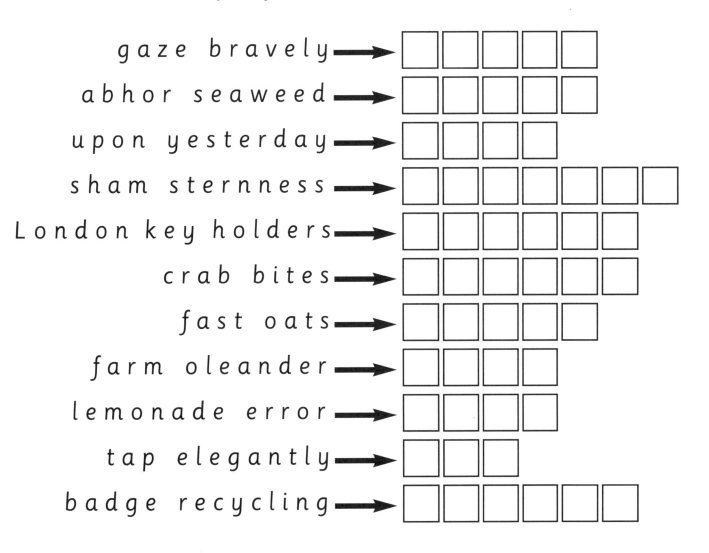

g a z e   b r a v e l y →

a b h o r   s e a w e e d →

u p o n   y e s t e r d a y →

s h a m   s t e r n n e s s →

L o n d o n   k e y   h o l d e r s →

c r a b   b i t e s →

f a s t   o a t s →

f a r m   o l e a n d e r →

l e m o n a d e   e r r o r →

t a p   e l e g a n t l y →

b a d g e   r e c y c l i n g →

Try to make up an animal puzzle of your own.

Football

1
Riddle

Can you solve this football riddle to find the name of an English football club?

Each clue gives two letters - one of these will help you to spell the name of a football club.

solution

My first in **eleven** is seen, also in **men** ....

My next is in **coach** but not **bench** and not **Sven** ....

My third is in **forward** and also in **cross**. ....

My fourth is in **water** and **draw**, not **coin** or **toss**. ....

My fifth, not in **extra**, is showing in **time**. ....

My sixth is in **match** and **pitch**, not **dirt** or **grime**. ....

My last, not in **talent** or **scout**, is in **search**. ....

I'm found in a city which has a large church.

The football club is ....

Try to make up a riddle of your own.

WET PLAY TODAY

Football

2
Riddle

Can you solve this football riddle to find the name of an English football club?

Each clue gives two letters - one of these will help you to spell the name of a football club.

solution

My first is in **referee** never in **side**. ....

My next is seen in **defence**, **saved** and **wide**. ....

My third is in **Charlton** and also in **Jack**. ....

My fourth is in **head** but not **talent** or **knack**. ....

My fifth is in **line** and is also in **wing**. ....

My sixth is in **fans** and in **chants** and in **sing**. ....

My last is in **Goran** and **game**, not **decision**. ....

I'm found west of London, could be 1st division!

The football club is ....

Try to make up a riddle of your own.

Football

3

Riddle

Can you solve this football riddle to find the name of an English football club?

Each clue gives two letters - one of these will help you to spell the name of a football club.

solution

My first is in **winner** and also in **draw**. ....

My next, not in **rule** or **book**, shows up in **law**. ....

My third is in **match** and in **team** and in **time**. ....

My fourth is in **foul** and **fall**, not **dive** or **crime**. ....

My fifth is in **cross** and **throw**, never in **save**. ....

My sixth is in **cheer** and **scream** but not in **wave**. ....

My last, not in **crisps** and **cans**, is found in **drinks**. ....

My all with an ex-England coach once had links.

The football club is ....

Try to make up a riddle of your own.

    WET PLAY TODAY

Football
ANSWERS
Riddle

Riddle 1

solution

My first in **eleven** is seen, and in **men** ...... en ...... n

My next is in **coach** but not **bench** and not Sven ...... oa ...... o

My third is in **forward** and also in **cross**. ...... or ...... r

My fourth is in **water** and **draw**, not **coin** or **toss**. ...... wa ...... w

My fifth, not in **extra**, is showing in **time**. ...... im i

My sixth is in **match** and **pitch**, not **dirt** or **grime**. ...... ch c

My last, not in **talent** or **scout**, is in **search**. ...... rh ...... h

I'm found in a city which has a large church.

Football Club:
NORWICH

Riddle 2

solution

My first is in **referee** never in **side**. ...... rf ...... r

My next is seen in **defence**, **saved** and **wide**. ...... de ...... e

My third is in **Charlton** and also in **Jack**. ...... ca ...... a

My fourth is in **head** but not **talent** or **knack**. ...... hd ...... d

My fifth is in **line** and is also in **wing**. ...... in i

My sixth is in **fans** and in **chants** and in **sing**. ...... ns ...... n

My last is in **Goran** and **game**, not **decision**. ...... ga ...... g

I'm found west of London, could be 1st division!

Football Club:
READING

Riddle 3

solution

My first is in **winner** and also in **draw**. ...... wr ...... w

My next, not in **rule** or **book**, shows up in **law**. ...... aw ...... a

My third is in **match** and in **team** and in **time**. ...... mt ...... t

My fourth is in **foul** and **fall**, not **dive** or **crime**. ...... fl ...... f

My fifth is in **cross** and **throw**, never in **save**. ...... ro ...... o

My sixth is in **cheer** and **scream** but not in **wave**. ...... cr ...... r

My last, not in **crisps** and **cans**, is found in **drinks**. ...... dk ...... d

My all with an ex-England coach once had links.

Football Club:
WATFORD

Missing Letters

Look at these two words.

There are nearly the same letters in each word.

CARBON   **CARTON**

The letters that have changed from one word to the next are B and T.

For each pair of words below, find the two letters that are different. Then choose the correct one of these letters to make the words of a short sentence. The first one is done for you.

		TWO LETTERS		ONE LETTER
READING	RAIDING	E | I	→	
RAIL	RAID		→	
STRIKE	STROKE		→	
BEAR	BEAK		→	
BEARD	BOARD		→	
CARTON	CARBON		→	
TOWER	TOWEL		→	
RUIN	REIN		→	
MATHS	MYTHS		→	
LAKE	LATE		→	
LATER	LAYER		→	
SPELLING	SPILLING		→	
WHIMPER	WHISPER		→	
WEAVER	WAIVER		→	

This sentence says:_____

WET PLAY TODAY

Find the Opposite

Here's the
first word.

Which one of these words means
the opposite of the first word?

Answer

| kind | type   mean   sleep   pretty   good | |

Now try these:

| up | mountain   high   low   down   hill | |

| on | if   off   in   out   up | |

| dark | white   black   brown   clear   light | |

| heavy | light   strong   weight   small   weak | |

| north | west   Arctic   south   east   Antarctic | |

| take | get   give   sell   collect   make | |

| sleep | dream   waking   awake   wake   woke | |

| sink | swim   float   bath   tap   dive | |

Try to make up your own opposite puzzle,
then ask one of your friends to solve it:

First word   Five words to choose from.

| | | | | | |

Find the Opposite - ANSWERS

Answer

| kind | type   mean   sleep   pretty   good | mean |

Now try these:

| up | mountain   high   low   down   hill | down |

| on | if   off   in   out   up | off |

| dark | white   black   brown   clear   light | light |

| heavy | light   strong   weight   small   weak | light |

| north | west   Arctic   south   east   Antarctic | south |

| take | get   give   sell   collect   make | give |

| sleep | dream   waking   awake   wake   woke | wake |

| sink | swim   float   bath   tap   dive | float |

   WET PLAY TODAY

Continue the Pattern (1)

Can you see the pattern on each line?

Continue the pattern.

Try to make your own pattern.

Continue the Pattern (2)

Can you see the pattern on each line?

Continue the pattern.

Try to make your own pattern.

WET PLAY TODAY

Clock Patience

A game for one person.
You will need a pack of playing cards.

The idea of this game is to get all your cards in their correct pile together, before you have turned up the four kings.

1. Make a circle of 12 cards, all face down and place one card in the middle of the circle.
2. Now continue placing all of the cards on top of these 13 cards, going around the circle to each pile in turn. There should now be 4 cards in each pile, including the central pile.
3. You are trying to put your cards in the correct place for a clock face. See the diagram.
4. Turn over the top card of the centre pile and place it on top of the correct pile for the number that it is.
5. Take the card from the bottom of that same pile and turn it over. Move this card to the top of the pile for its correct number.
6. Continue like this. Whenever you turn over a king, it goes onto the centre pile.
   When all the kings are in the centre, the game is over. Try again!

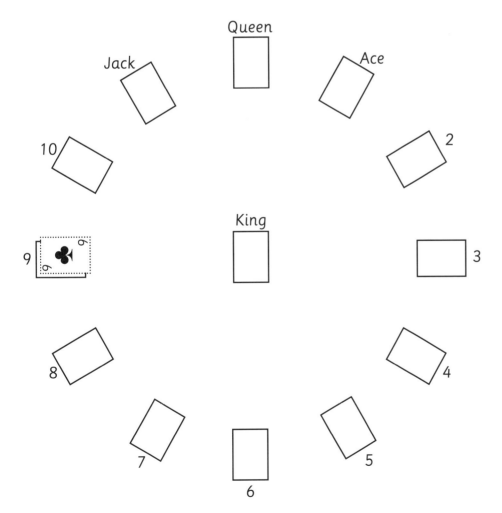

If the first card you turned over from the centre pile was a '9' then you would place it on top of the pile at the '9' position of the clock of cards. Then you take the card from the bottom of the '9' pile and move it to its correct 'clock' position.

Now and Venn

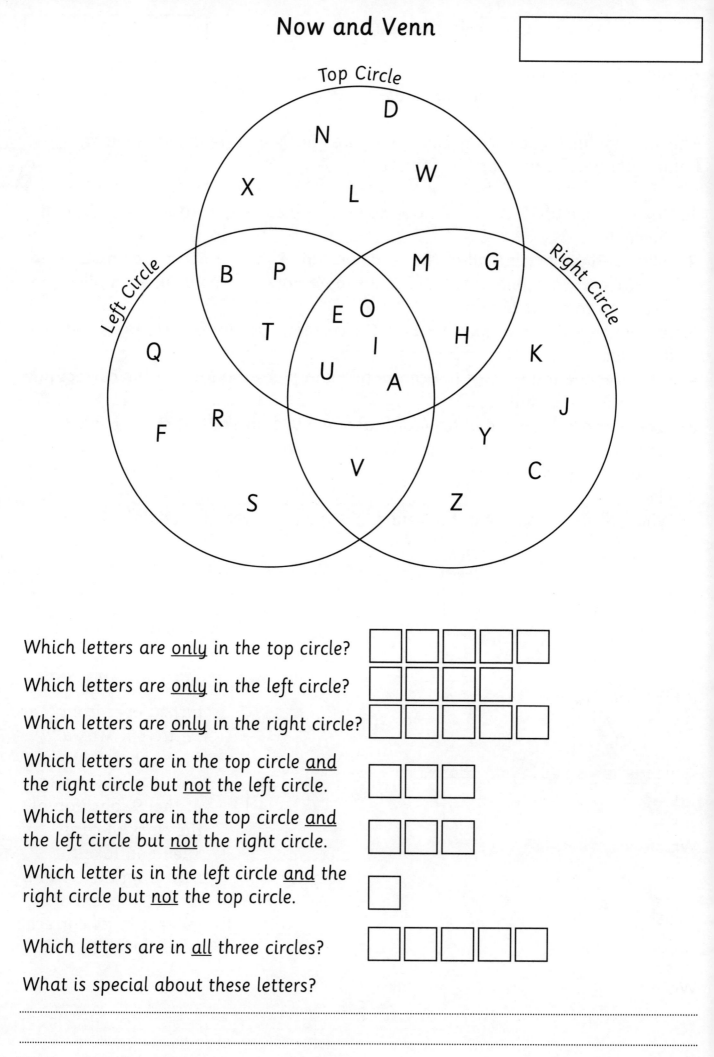

Top Circle

Left Circle

Right Circle

D
N
X
W
L
B P
M G
T
E O
I
H
Q
U
A
K
R
F
J
Y
V
C
S
Z

Which letters are <u>only</u> in the top circle?

Which letters are <u>only</u> in the left circle?

Which letters are <u>only</u> in the right circle?

Which letters are in the top circle <u>and</u> the right circle but <u>not</u> the left circle.

Which letters are in the top circle <u>and</u> the left circle but <u>not</u> the right circle.

Which letter is in the left circle <u>and</u> the right circle but <u>not</u> the top circle.

Which letters are in <u>all</u> three circles?

What is special about these letters?

....

....

       WET PLAY TODAY

Where are the Letters?

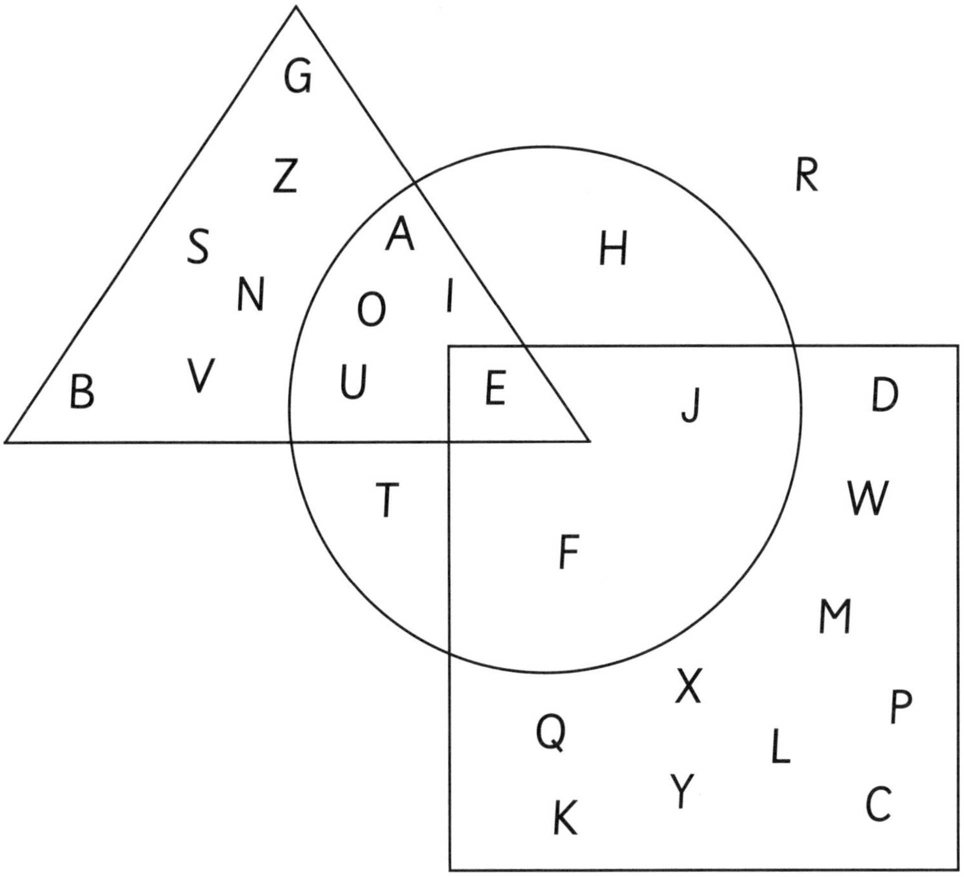

Which letters are in the triangle <u>and</u> the circle but <u>not</u> in the square?

▢ ▢ ▢ ▢

Which letters are in the square and the circle but not the triangle?

▢ ▢

Which letter is in all three shapes?

▢

Which letter is not in any shape?

▢

Which letters are in the circle only?

▢ ▢

Which letters are in the triangle only?

▢ ▢ ▢ ▢ ▢ ▢

Which letters are in the square only?

▢ ▢ ▢ ▢ ▢ ▢ ▢ ▢ ▢

Joining Squares

Here are six different patterns made with 3 squares.

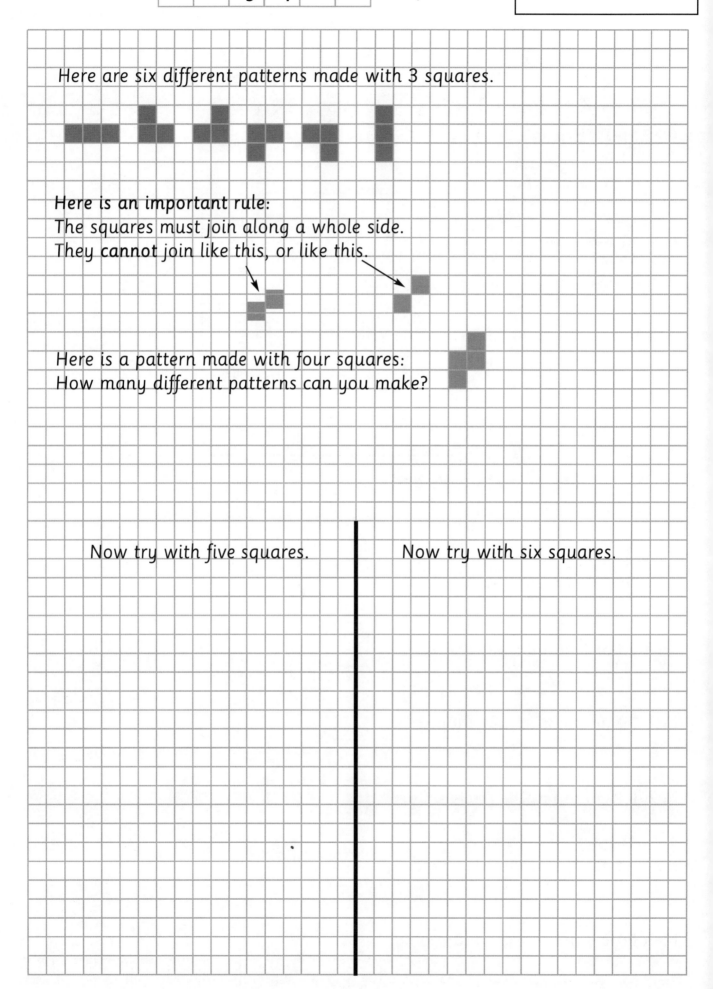

Here is an important rule:
The squares must join along a whole side.
They **cannot** join like this, or like this.

Here is a pattern made with four squares:
How many different patterns can you make?

Now try with five squares.

Now try with six squares.

© Andrew Brodie Publications   www.acblack.com

WET PLAY TODAY

Tessellation

These shapes tessellate:

So do these:

Colour a tessellating pattern on the grid below.
Cover as much of the grid as you can.

Hexagons

Here is a regular hexagon: It is made of six triangles.

Using the equilateral triangles, try to make a bigger regular hexagon.

How many triangles is it made from?

Try to find a bigger one. How may triangles now?

Try an even bigger one, then count the triangles.

   WET PLAY TODAY

Mobius Strip

✂ Cut out the strip on this page.

✏ Draw a line down the centre of the strip. Your line is only on one side of the paper.

➷ Twist the strip once and then form it into a loop. (See diagram)

❐ Stick or tape the ends of the strip together.

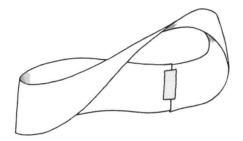

✏ Now draw another line down the centre of the strip using a different colour pen. Start your line where the strip joins and keep going until you get back to the same place.

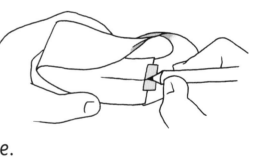

❢ What do you notice about this line?

✂ Make a slit on this new line and cut along it right the way round.

❢ How many loops do you think you will have?

✂ You could try cutting this new loop down the centre.

➷ Try again, but this time with a longer strip of paper. Put 2 twists in the first loop.

Idioms

Here are some examples of expressions known as idioms:

> ♣ over the moon
> ♣ see the light
> ♣ bear with a sore head
> ♣ pull your socks up
> ♣ beat about the bush
> ♣ can't see for looking
> ♣ drive me up the wall

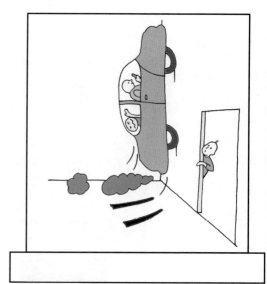

Can you guess the two shown here?

Draw a picture to illustrate an idiom and see if your friend can guess which one it represents.

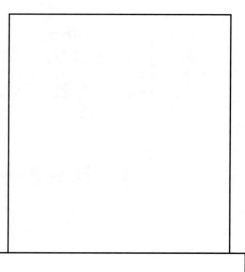

Can you think of some more? ....

....

WET PLAY TODAY

Number Frames (1)

Use the numbers given to complete the frame.

There is only one way to complete each puzzle.

2 digits	3 digits	4 digits
99	708	1234
26	711	3102
33	309	5303

5 digits	6 digits
41158	689108
75652	

Number Frames (2)

Use the numbers given to complete the frame.

There is only one way to complete each puzzle.

2 digits	3 digits	4 digits
11	037	1789
29	216	4031
32	372	4982
53	627	6935
88	695	
97	768	

5 digits	6 digits	7 digits
41828	814327	3421767
46802		
67302		
85703		

© Andrew Brodie Publications   www.acblack.com   WET PLAY TODAY

Number Frames - ANSWERS

Frame 1

7	5	6	5	2	■	3	3
■	■	8	■	■	■	■	0
■	■	9	■	■	■	9	9
■	4	1	1	5	8	■	■
■	■	0	■	3	■	■	■
7	0	8	■	0	■	■	■
1	■	■	■	3	1	0	2
1	2	3	4	■	■	■	6

Frame 2

1	7	8	9	■	■	4	9	8	2
■	■	1	■	■	■	6	■	■	9
■	■	4	1	8	2	8	■	■	■
4	0	3	1	■	■	0	3	7	■
■	■	2	■	3	7	2	■	6	■
6	2	7	■	2	■	■	■	8	8
7	■	■	■	■	■	■	■	■	5
3	4	2	1	7	6	7	■	9	7
0	■	1	■	■	9	■	■	■	0
2	■	6	9	3	5	■	■	5	3

Letter Code 1 (A)

Each number in the grid represents a letter of the alphabet.
For example, the number 7 on the grid will be the letter A.

Using the word given to help you begin, complete the crossword and the code at the bottom of the page.

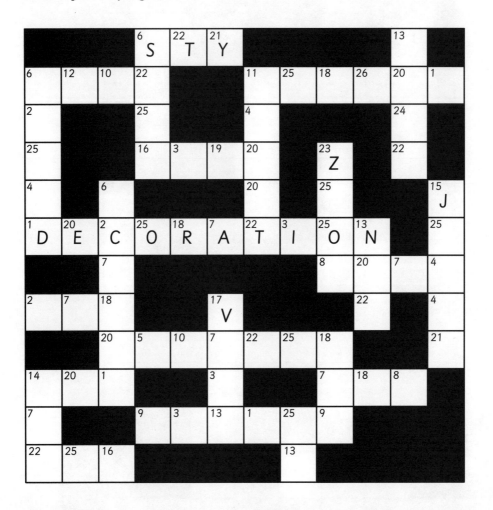

1	2	3	4	5	6	7	8	9	10	11	12	13
						A						

14	15	16	17	18	19	20	21	22	23	24	25	26

If you have cracked the code correctly you will easily be able to find the famous people on the next sheet.

WET PLAY TODAY

Letter Code 1 (B)

Using the code from the previous sheet, find the famous people below.

15 25 12 7 13 13   6 20 14 7 6 22 3 7 13   14 7 2 12   (Composer)

_ _ _ _ _ _   _ _ _ _ _ _ _ _ _   _ _ _ _

9 3 13 6 22 25 13   2 12 10 18 2 12 3 4 4   (British Politician)

_ _ _ _ _ _ _   _ _ _ _ _ _ _ _ _

9 17 4 22   1 3 6 13 20 21   (Film Maker)

_ _ _ _   _ _ _ _ _ _

2 12 18 3 6 22 25 16 12 20 18   2 25 4 10 8 14 10 6   (Explorer)

_ _ _ _ _ _ _ _ _ _ _   _ _ _ _ _ _ _

9 3 4 4 3 7 8   6 12 7 19 20 6 16 20 7 18 20   (Poet/Playwright)

_ _ _ _ _ _ _   _ _ _ _ _ _ _ _ _ _

20 4 17 3 6   16 18 20 6 4 20 21   (American Singer)

_ _ _ _ _   _ _ _ _ _ _ _

2 12 7 18 4 20 6   1 7 18 9 3 13   (Naturalist/Author of 'Origin of Species')

_ _ _ _ _ _ _   _ _ _ _ _ _

13 20 3 4   7 18 8 6 22 18 25 13 26   (1st human to step on moon)

_ _ _ _   _ _ _ _ _ _ _ _ _

15   19   18 25 9 4 3 16 26   (Author)

_ .   _ .   _ _ _ _ _ _ _ _

18 25 26 20 18   14 7 13 13 3 6 22 20 18   (1st to run a mile in under 4 minutes)

_ _ _ _ _   _ _ _ _ _ _ _ _ _

Letter Code 2 (A)

Each number in the grid represents a letter of the alphabet.
For example, the number 3 on the grid will be the letter A.

Using the word given to help you begin, complete the crossword and the code
at the bottom of the page.

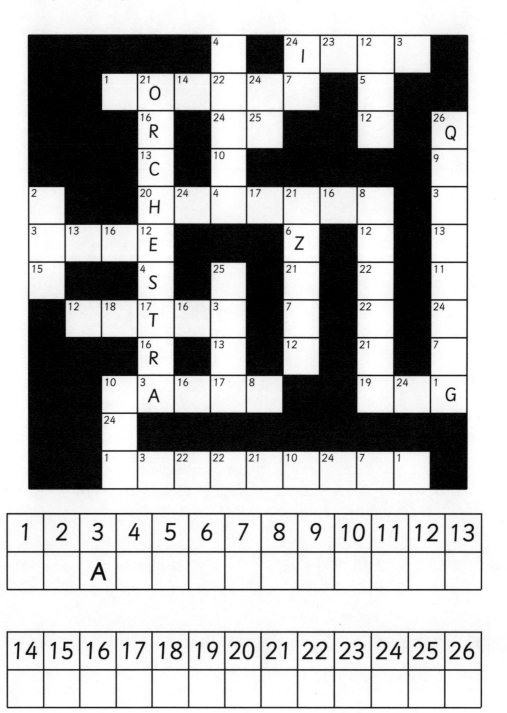

1	2	3	4	5	6	7	8	9	10	11	12	13
		A										

14	15	16	17	18	19	20	21	22	23	24	25	26

Now use the code to find the cities on the next sheet.

WET PLAY TODAY

Letter Code 2 (B)

If you have cracked the code correctly you should be able to find the name of 10 cities on this page and the counties in which they are situated.

① 13 3 7 14 12 16 16 3   3 9 4 17 16 3 22 24 3

_ _ _ _ _ _ _ _   _ _ _ _ _ _ _ _ _

② 22 21 7 23 21 7   12 7 1 22 3 7 23

_ _ _ _ _ _   _ _ _ _ _ _ _

③ 12 23 24 7 14 9 16 1 20   4 13 21 17 22 3 7 23

_ _ _ _ _ _ _ _ _   _ _ _ _ _ _ _ _

④ 16 21 15 12   24 17 3 22 8

_ _ _ _   _ _ _ _ _

⑤ 1 12 7 12 5 3   4 19 24 17 6 12 16 22 3 7 23

_ _ _ _ _ _   _ _ _ _ _ _ _ _ _ _ _

⑥ 13 21 10 12 7 20 3 1 12 7   23 12 7 15 3 16 11

_ _ _ _ _ _ _ _ _ _   _ _ _ _ _ _ _

⑦ 10 3 16 24 4   25 16 3 7 13 12

_ _ _ _ _   _ _ _ _ _ _

⑧ 19 3 4 20 24 7 1 17 21 7 23. 13.   9 7 24 17 12 23   4 17 3 17 12 4

_ _ _ _ _ _ _ _ _ _ _ _._ _._ _ _ _ _ _ _   _ _ _ _ _ _

                              21 25   3 15 12 16 24 13 3

                             _ _   _ _ _ _ _ _ _

⑨ 5 3 7 13 21 9 5 12 16   13 3 7 3 23 3

_ _ _ _ _ _ _ _ _   _ _ _ _ _ _

⑩ 14 3 16 13 12 22 21 7 3   4 10 3 24 7

_ _ _ _ _ _ _ _ _   _ _ _ _ _

Letter Code - ANSWERS

Letter Code 1 sheets A and B

1	2	3	4	5	6	7	8	9	10	11	12	13
D	C	I	L	Q	S	A	M	W	U	F	H	N

14	15	16	17	18	19	20	21	22	23	24	25	26
B	J	P	V	R	K	E	Y	T	Z	X	O	G

Famous People that should have been decoded:
Johann Sebastian Bach
Winston Churchill
Walt Disney
Christopher Columbus
William Shakespeare
Elvis Presley
Charles Darwin
Neil Armstrong
J. K. Rowling
Roger Bannister

Letter Code 2 sheets A and B

1	2	3	4	5	6	7	8	9	10	11	12	13
G	J	A	S	V	Z	N	Y	U	P	K	E	C

14	15	16	17	18	19	20	21	22	23	24	25	26
B	M	R	T	X	W	H	O	L	D	I	F	Q

10 cities and their countries.
Canberra - Australia
London - England
Edinburgh - Scotland
Rome - Italy
Geneva - Switzerland
Copenhagen - Denmark
Paris - France
Washington D.C. - United States of America
Vancouver - Canada
Barcelona - Spain

     WET PLAY TODAY

Magic Squares

In a magic square the numbers in every row, column and diagonal always add up to the same number.

Look carefully at this example:

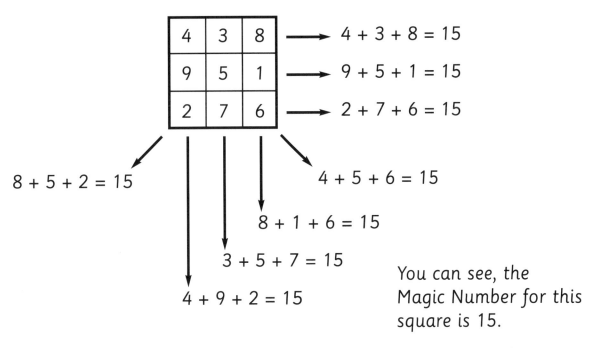

4 + 3 + 8 = 15

9 + 5 + 1 = 15

2 + 7 + 6 = 15

8 + 5 + 2 = 15

4 + 5 + 6 = 15

8 + 1 + 6 = 15

3 + 5 + 7 = 15

4 + 9 + 2 = 15

You can see, the Magic Number for this square is 15.

The magic squares below have some missing numbers. To find the missing numbers, follow these steps:

Step 1: Find the Magic Number by adding a row, column or diagonal which has no missing numbers.

Step 2: Look for a row, column or diagonal which has only one missing number.

Step 3: Add the other numbers in the row, column or diagonal which you have chosen, then subtract this total from the Magic Number. You now have the number which will complete that line.

Step 4: Keep working by always looking for a line with only one missing number.

5		9
10		
3		

Magic Number=

		7
	8	13
9		

Magic Number=

		8
5		9
		4

Magic Number=

11		18
	14	
10		

Magic Number=

5mm Square Grid

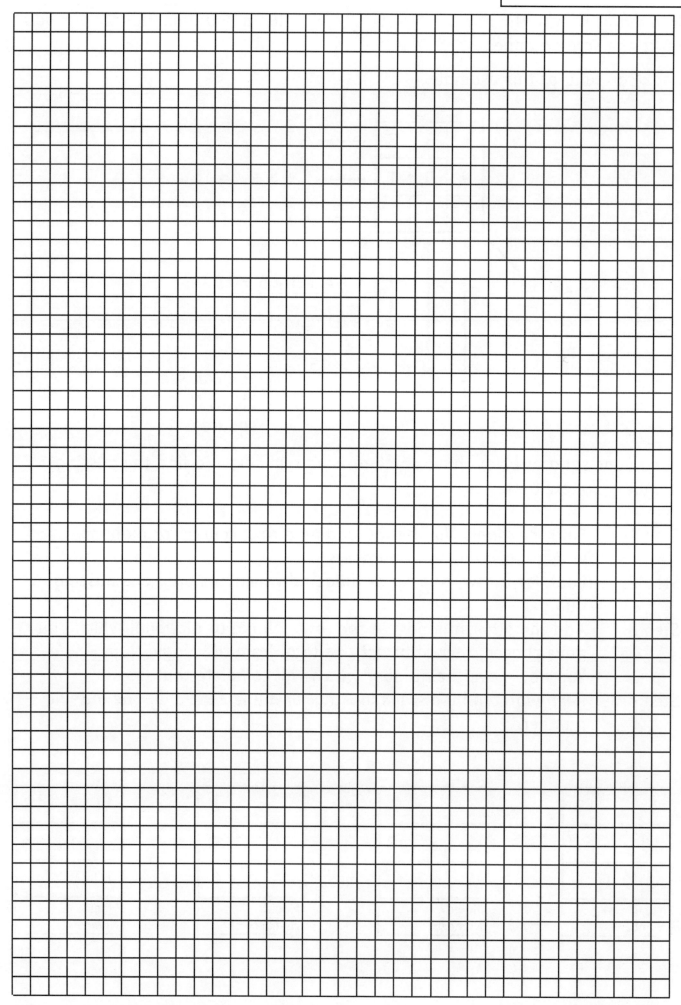

76

WET PLAY TODAY

10mm Square Grid

10mm Dotty Square Grid

WET PLAY TODAY

10mm Dotty Triangle Grid

Equilateral Triangle Grid

© Andrew Brodie Publications   www.acblack.com   WET PLAY TODAY